GW00656609

Exclusive Distributors

International Music Publications Limited, Southend Road, Woodford Green, Essex IG8 8HN, England

International Music Publications Limited, 25 Rue D'Hautville, 75010 Paris, France

International Music Publications GmbH, Germany, Marstallstraße 8, D-80539 Munchen, Germany

Nuova Carish S.R.L., Via M.F. Quintiliano 40, 20138 Milano, Italy

Danmusik, Vognmagergade 7, DK-1120 Copenhagen K, Denmark

Warner/Chappell Music Inc, Australia, 1 Cassins Avenue, North Sydney, New South Wales 2060, Australia

Folio © 1997 International Music Publications Ltd
Southend Road, Woodford Green, Essex IG8 8HN

Music Transcribed by Barnes Music Engraving Ltd., East Sussex TN22 4HA
Printed by The Panda Group · Haverhill · Suffolk CB9 8PR · UK · Binding by ABS · Cambridge

Photo's Pages 2, 3, 30, 31 Liz Johnson-Artur

Beetlebum

Beetlebum
What you done
She's a gun
Now what you've done
Beetlebum
Get nothing done
You beetlebum
Just get numb
Now what you've done
Beetlebum

And when she lets me slip away
She turns me on all my violence is gone
Nothing is wrong
I just slip away and I am gone
Nothing is wrong
She turns me on
I just slip away and now I am gone

Beetlebum
Because you're young
She's a gun
Now what you've done
Beetlebum
She'll suck your thumb
She'll make you cum'
Coz' she's your gun
Now what you've done
Beetlebum

He's on, he's on, he's on it

Song 2

I got my head checked
By a jumbo jet
It wasn't easy but nothing is
no

When I feel heavy metal
And I'm pins and I'm needles
Well, I lie and I'm easy
All the time but I am never sure
why I need you
Pleased to meet you

I got my head down
When I was young
It's not my problem
It's not my problem

When I feel heavy metal
And I'm pins and I'm needles
Well, I lie and I'm easy
All the time but I am never sure
why I need you
Pleased to meet you

Yeah Yeah
Yeah Yeah
Yeah Yeah
Oh Yeah

Country Sad Ballad Man

Yeah I found no where
It got to know me
Let me sleep all day
Spent the money
I haven't felt my legs
Since the summer
And I don't call my friends
Forgot their numbers

VIP 223
Have my chances
They have me
Now stay up nights
Watch TV
I'm country sad
I'm a ballad man

I'm on the come back road
Yeah I'm a bizzard
And in my motor home
Sweat on my pillow all night

I'm a ballad man . . .

M.O.R.

It's automatic
I need to unload
Under the pressure
Gone middle of the road
Fall into fashion
Fall out again
We stick together
Cause it never ends

Here comes a low
I'm a boy and you're a girl
Here comes a high
The only ones in the world
Here comes everything
You and me can work it out
Here it comes
You Me, we'll work it out!

Here comes tomorrow
1 2 3 episodes
The middle of the road
Cause that's entertainment
It's the sound of the wheel
It rolls on forever
You know how it feels

Here comes a low
I'm a boy and you're a girl
Here comes a high
The only one that's in the world
Here comes everything
We're like monkeys out in space
Here it comes
You Me, we'll work it out!

It's automatic
I need to unload
Under the pressure
Gone middle of the road
Fall into fashion
Fall out again
We stick together
Cause it never ends

Here comes a low
I'm a boy and you're a girl
Here comes a high
You're the one that's in the world
Here comes everything
You and me can work it out
Here it comes
You Me, we'll work it out!

On Your Own

Holy man tiptoed his way across the gange
The sound of magic music in his ear
Videod by a bus load of tourist
Shiny shellsuits on and drinking lemonad
Now I got a funny feeling which I bought mailorde
From a man in a teepee in Californi
Said he once was that great game show performe
Then he blew all his money awa
Blew it all awa

So take me hom
don't leave me alon
I'm not that goo
But I am not that ba
No psycho kille
Hooligan guerrill
I dream to ric
Oh you should try
I'll eat parole get gold card sou
My joy of life is on a ro
And we'll all be the same in the en

Then you're on your own (2

Well we all go happy day glow in the disco
The sound of magic music in our brain
Someone stumbles to the bathroom with the horror
Says' Lord give me time for I've jumped into spac
I'm in outer spac

So take me hom
don't leave me alon
I'm not that goo
But I am not that ba
No psycho kille
Hooligan guerrill
I dream to ric
Oh you should try
I'll eat parole get gold card sou
My joy of life is on a ro
And we'll all be the same in the en

Then you're on your own (2

You're So Grea

Sad drunk and poorl
Sleeping really lat
Sad drunk and poorl
Not feeling so grea
Wondering lost in a town full of frown
Sad drunk and poorl
Dogs digging up the groun

And I feel the light in the night and in the da
And I feel the light when the sky's just mud and gre
And I feel the night when you tell me it's oka
Coz' you're so great and I love yo

Tea, Tea and Coffe
Helps to start the da
Tea, Tea and Coffe
Shaking all the wa
Cities alive, a surprise so am
Tea, Tea and Coffee, get no sleep toda

And I feel the light in the night and in the da
And I feel the light when the sky's just mud and gre
And I feel the night when you tell me it's oka
Coz' you're so great and I love you

Death of a Party

The death of the party
Came as no surprise
Why did we bother
Should have stayed away

Another night
And I thought well well
Go to another party
And hang myself
Gently on the shelf

The death of the teenager
Standing on his own
Why did he bother
Should have slept alone

Another night
And I thought well well
Go to another party
And hang myself
Gently on the shelf

(Repeat)

Chinese Bombs

He makes an inner arm block
Then kicks from behind
The lights they go off
But he can fight blind
Coz' he got the touch
But he won't live long
Coz' he comes from Hong Kong
Where people are strong

Chinese Bombs, millions jump, chairman's junk, USA
Won't Somebody, Won't Somebody
Sink the place

Got a cab to go to Soho
The dragon says go
Let everyone know
You got the touch
You come from Hong Kong
Where people are strong
And you won't live long

Chinese Bombs, millions jump, chairman's junk to Hong Kong, USA
Won't Somebody, Won't Somebody
Bruce Lee comes to save the day
Bruce Lee comes the Chinese way

I'm Just a Killer for Your Love

I heard a man who had no lungs
He took me in and made me lunch
He told me how I'd lost a friend
He smiled at me it was the end
I said

I'm just a killer for your love (4)

I cut my hair off in the road
I take my coat off dropped my load
I wipe my hands on the grass
Coz' I know that nothing ever lasts
And I said

I'm just a killer for your love (4)

Look Inside America

Good morning lethargy
Drink pepsi is good for energy
The bath's on, smoke in the bedroom
Sore throat and on my neck a nasty bruise
Where it came from, well I don't know
We played last night, it was a good show

Got the play out on a second rate chatshow
It's a nationwide deal, so we gotta go
Chuck from the company says it'll be alright
Got an add on K-ROQ and there's an instore tonight
Well I build things up
Then I let them go
Got to get time share on the radio

Look inside America, she's alright, she's alright
Sitting out the distance but I'm not trying to make up her mind
Looking for America
With its kookie nights and suicide
Where the TV says it's alright
Coz' everybody's hung up on something or other

"Steppin' off in 20" so the driver says
I should sleep tonight but I think I'll watch videos instead
Annie Hall leaves NY in the end
Press rewind Woody gets her back again
And the whole world could have passed thru' me
But I don't know if it means that much to me

And the whole world could have passed thru' me
But I don't know if it means that much to me

Movin' On

At the music heist
I met the gourmet man
With aluminium lungs
Sucks out all he can

Seek the whole world go flip
In a stunt bug style
He's a parasite
With a cellulite pile
But he can smile

This is the music
And we're movin' on, we're moving on

We're sticky eyes and sticky bones
you get no time on your own
you get a dose and a ghost

You get it coast to coast
dye your hair black
get satan tattooed on your back
pierce yourself with a coke can
put yourself in fake tan now you're in the band

Coz' this is the music
and we're movin' on, we're movin' on
Hey this is the music
and we're movin' on, we're movin' on
no matter how low, there's always further to go
We're movin' on, we're movin' on

We're movin' on, it won't be long
We're movin' on, it won't be long

Essex Dogs

I remember thinkin' murder in the car
Watching dogs somersault through sprinklers on tiny lawns
I remember the graffiti, we are your children coming in with spray cans of paint
I remember the sunset and the plains of cement
And the way the night seems to turn the colour of orangeade

In this town cellular phones are hot with thieves
In this town we all go to terminal pubs
It helps us sweat out those angry bits of life
From this town the English Army grind their teeth to glass
You'll get a kicking tonight
Smell of puke and piss
Smell of puke and piss on your stilettos

Here comes that panic attack
My heart stops, then it starts
Give me a drink
I'll drink your round
I'll take you round the pole
It's cold up here
You'll catch the flu or you'll catch the city
either way you'll catch the flu
or you'll catch the city

Strange News From Another Star

All I want to be is washed out by the sea
No death star over me
Won't give me any peace
All I want is light relief
Put the crazies on the street
Give the guns and feed them meat
Now shoot the death star down
Dig a hole and put it down
Thousand miles underground

They say it's no game
there's strange news from another star
I'm lost, I'm lost
there's strange news from another star

Give me all your stuff
until I can't get up
Watch the whole world freeze
Counting tin cans in our sleep
Submarines are diving deep
I don't believe in me
I don't believe in me
All I've ever done is tame
Will you love me all the same
Will you love me, though
always the same

They say it's no game
there's strange news from another star
I'm lost, I'm lost
there's strange news from another star

Beetlebum

Songs: Albarn
Music: Albarn, Coxon, James, Rowntree

Song 2

Songs: Albarn
Music: Albarn, Coxon, James, Rowntree

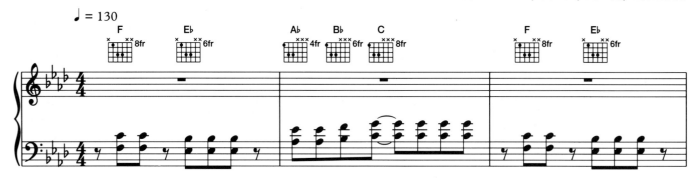

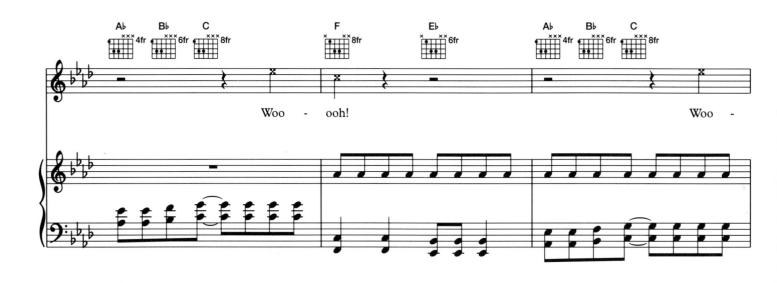

Woo - ooh!   Woo -

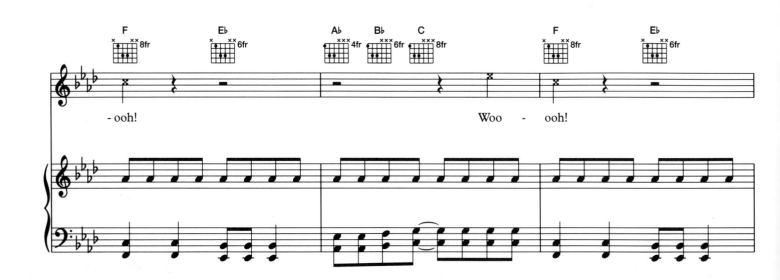

- ooh!   Woo - ooh!

Country Sad Ballad Man

Songs: Albarn
Music: Albarn, Coxon, James, Rowntree

man.

Instrumental ad lib.

M.O.R.

Songs: Albarn
Music: Albarn, Coxon, James, Rowntree

On Your Own

Songs: Albarn
Music: Albarn, Coxon, James, Rowntree

Theme From Retro

Songs: Albarn
Music: Albarn, Coxon, James, Rowntree

You're So Great

Song and Music: Coxon

'Cause you're so great and I love you.____

'Cause you're so great and I love you.

Death Of A Party

Songs: Albarn
Music: Albarn, Coxon, James, Rowntree

gent - ly on___ the shelf.___

The death

Chinese Bombs

Songs: Albarn
Music: Albarn, Coxon, James, Rowntree

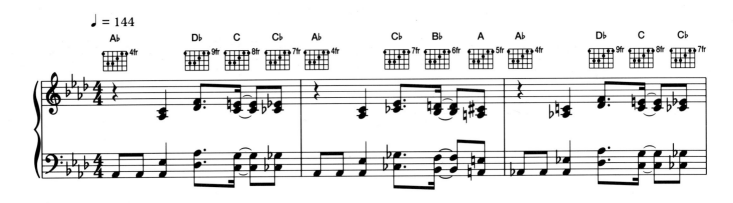

He makes an in-ner arm
cab to go to So-

block, then kicks from be-hind. The lights they go off, but he can fight
-ho, the dra-gon says go. Let ev-ery-one know you got the

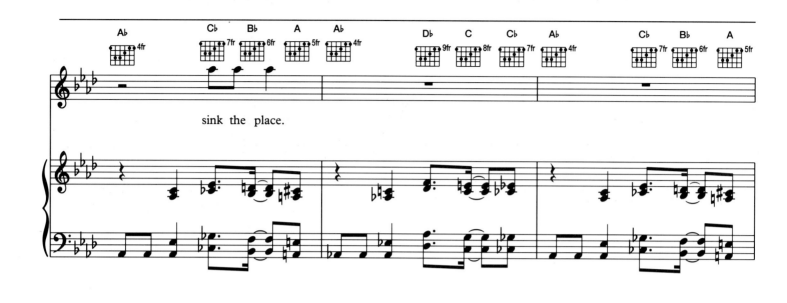

sink the place.

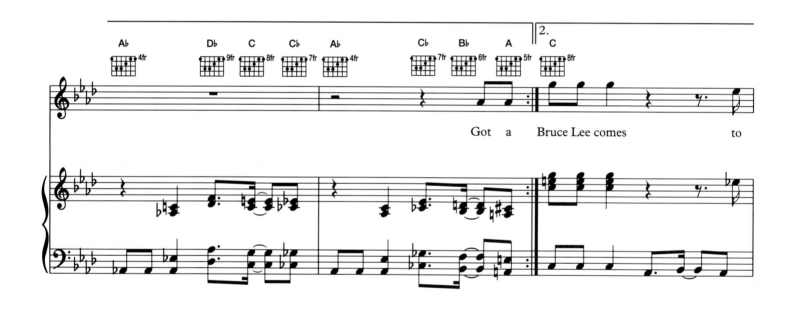

Got a Bruce Lee comes to

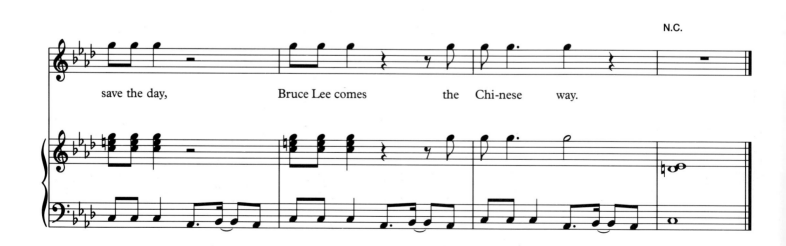

save the day, Bruce Lee comes the Chi-nese way.

I'm Just A Killer For Your Love

Songs: Albarn
Music: Albarn, Coxon, James, Rowntree

repeat to fade

Look Inside America

Songs: Albarn
Music: Albarn, Coxon, James, Rowntree

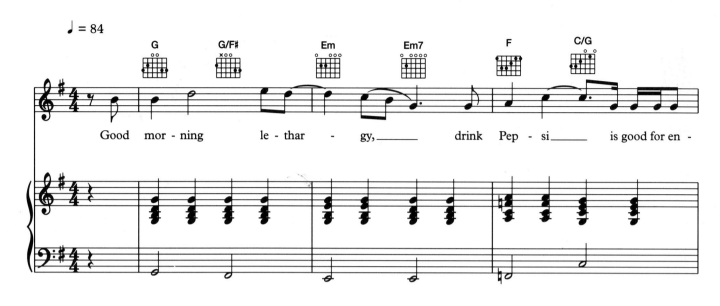

Good mor - ning le - thar - gy,_____ drink Pep - si_____ is good for en -

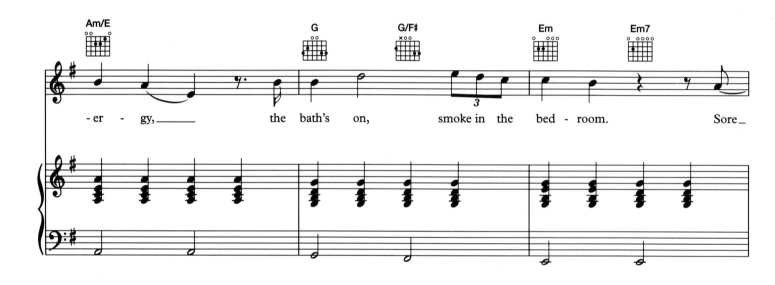

-er - gy,_____ the bath's on, smoke in the bed - room. Sore_

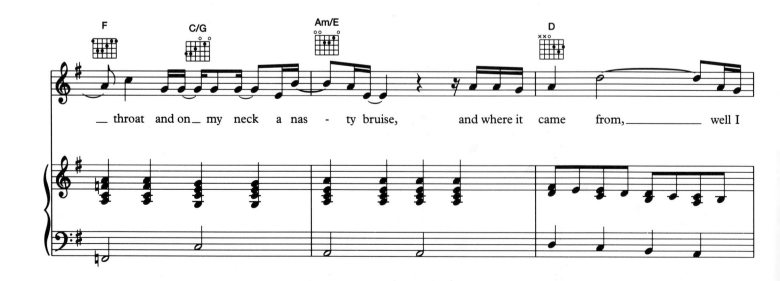

throat and on my neck a nas - ty bruise, and where it came from,_____ well I

48

Strange News From Another Star

Songs: Albarn
Music: Albarn, Coxon, James, Rowntree

Movin' On

Songs: Albarn
Music: Albarn, Coxon, James, Rowntree

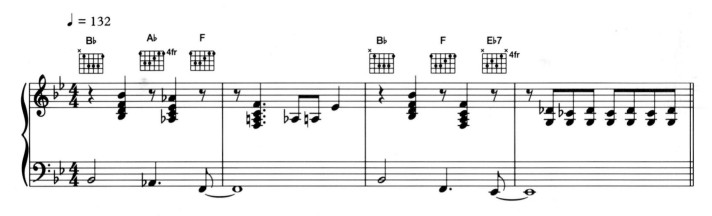

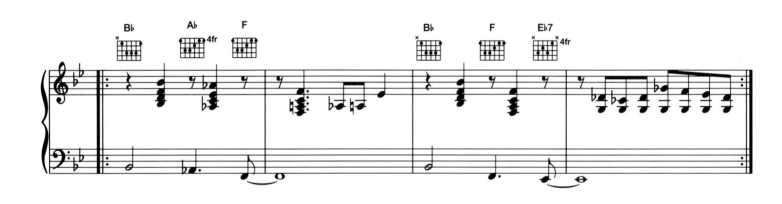

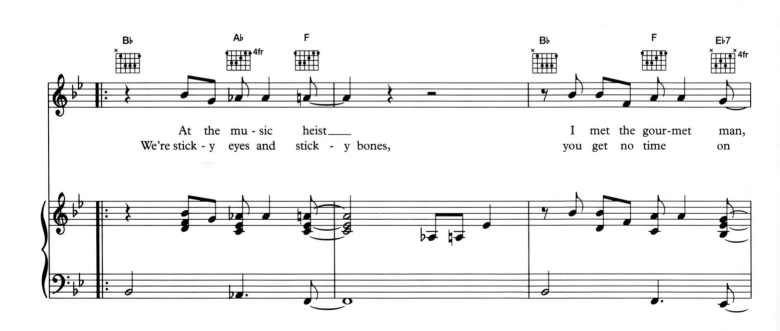

At the mu - sic heist___ I met the gour-met man,
We're stick - y eyes and stick - y bones, you get no time on

Essex Dogs

Songs: Albarn
Music: Albarn, Coxon, James, Rowntree

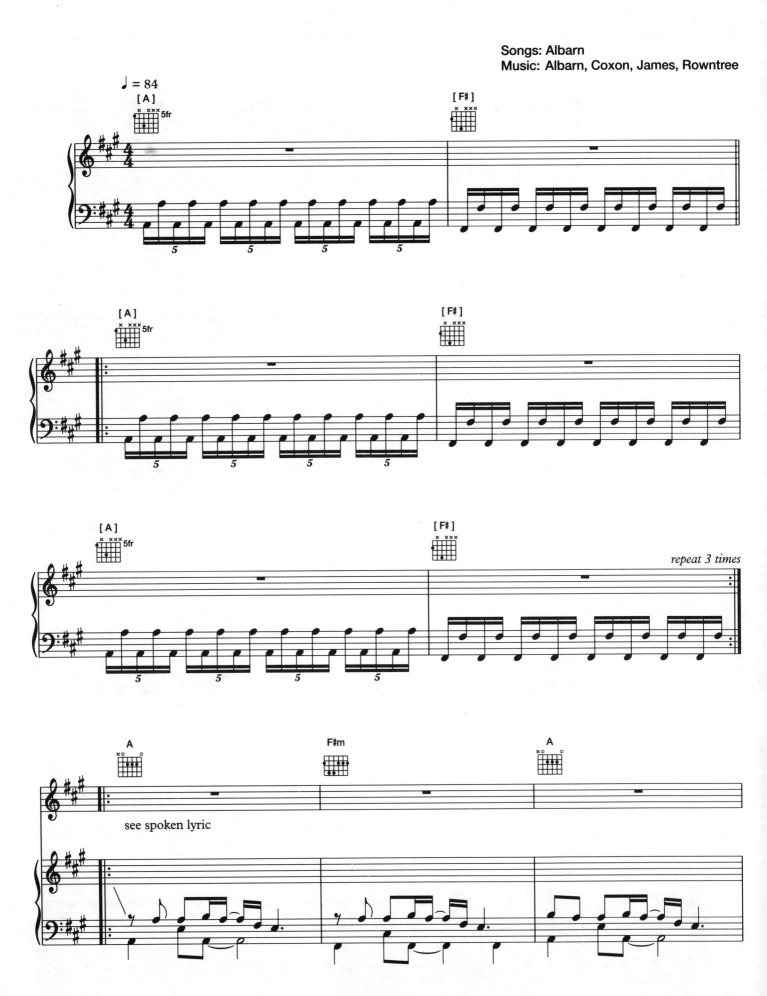

Spoken:

1 I remember thinkin' murder in the car
   Watching dogs somersault through sprinklers on tiny lawns
   I remember the graffitti, we are your children coming in with spray cans of paint
   I remember the sunset and the plains of cement
   And the way the night seems to turn the colour of orangeade

2 In this town cellular phones are hot with thieves
   In this town we all go to terminal pubs
   It helps us sweat out those angry bits of life
   From this town the English Army grind their teeth to glass
   You'll get a kicking tonight, smell of puke and piss
   Smell of puke and piss on your stilettos

3 Here comes that panic attack, my heart stops, then it starts
   Give me a drink, I'll drink your round
   I'll take you round the pole, it's cold up here
   You'll catch the flu or you'll catch the city
   Either way you'll catch the flu, or you'll catch the city

Printed in England
The Panda Group · Haverhill · Suffolk · 5/97